CLASSICAL
PIANO SOLOS
COLLECTION

VOLUME *THREE*

Wise Publications
London / New York / Paris / Sydney / Copenhagen / Madrid

Exclusive Distributors:

Music Sales Limited
8/9 Frith Street, London W1V 5TZ, England.

Music Sales Pty Limited
120 Rothschild Avenue, Rosebery, NSW 2018, Australia.

Music Sales Corporation
257 Park Avenue South, New York, NY10010, United States of America.

Order No. AM91536
ISBN 0-7119-3758-3
This book © Copyright 1994 by Wise Publications

Unauthorised reproduction of any part of this publication by
any means including photocopying is an infringement of Copyright.

Book design by Studio Twenty, London
Computer management by Adam Hay Editorial Design
Compiled by Stephen Harding

Printed in the United Kingdom by
J.B. Offset Printers (Marks Tey) Limited, Marks Tey, Essex.

Rumores de la Caleta, Malagueña, No.6
from Recuerdos de Viaje

Composed by Isaac Albéniz

Dal 𝄋 al Fine

7

Invention No.4 in D Minor
BWV775

Composed by Johann Sebastian Bach

Piano Sonata No.25 in G Major
Op.79 - 1st Movement

Composed by Ludwig van Beethoven

Nocturne in E♭
Op. 9, No. 2

Composed by Frédéric Chopin

Intermezzo in A Major
Op.118, No.2

Composed by Johannes Brahms

21

Air And Variations
The Harmonious Blacksmith from Suite No.5

Composed by George Frideric Handel

Var. 2

Var. 3

Var. 4

Var. 5

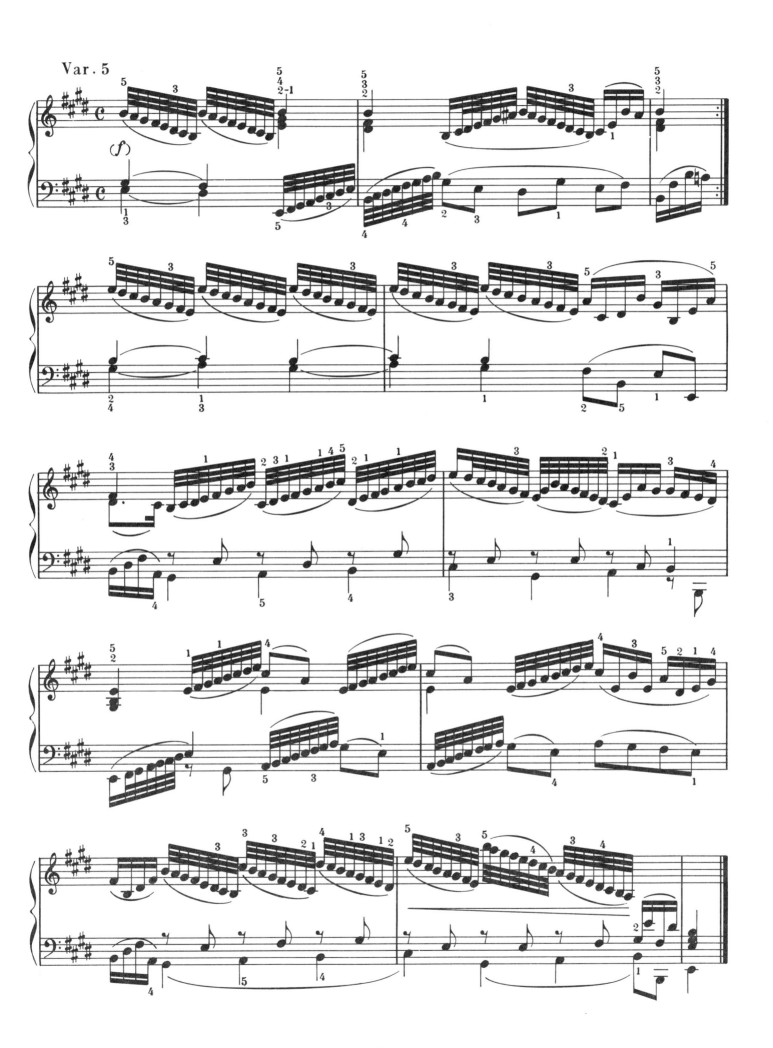

Consolation No.3 in D♭ Major

Composed by Franz Liszt

Venetian Gondola Song
Op.30, No.6
from Songs Without Words

Composed by Felix Mendelssohn-Bartholdy

Doctor Gradus ad Parnassum No.1
from The Children's Corner Suite

Composed by Claude Debussy

Modérément animé

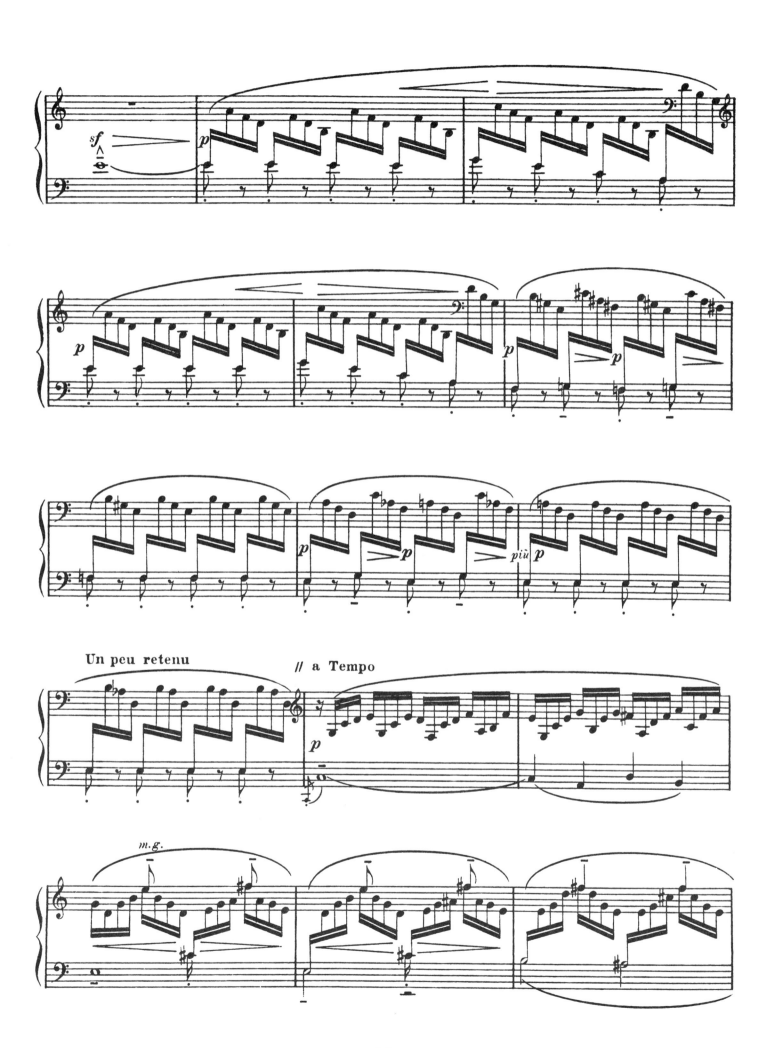

Très animé

Fantasia in D Minor
K.397

Composed by Wolfgang Amadeus Mozart

Allegretto

Prelude, Op.23, No.6

Composed by Lennox Berkeley

43

Moment Musical in F Minor
Op.94, No.3

Composed by Franz Schubert

Humoresque
Op.10, No.2

Composed by Peter Ilyich Tchaikovsky

Here in Volume Three *of this distinctive series...*

Air And Variations - The Harmonious Blacksmith from Suite No.5 Handel
Consolation No.3 in D♭ Major Liszt
Doctor Gradus ad Parnassum No.1 from The Children's Corner Suite Debussy
Fantasia in D Minor, K.397 Mozart
Humoresque, Op.10, No.2 Tchaikovsky
Intermezzo in A Major, Op.118, No.2 Brahms
Invention No.4 in D Minor, BWV775 Bach
Moment Musical in F Minor, Op.94, No.3 Schubert
Nocturne in E♭, Op.9, No.2 Chopin
Piano Sonata No.25 in G Major, Op.79 - 1st Movement Beethoven
Prelude, Op.23, No.6 Berkeley
Rumores de la Caleta, Malagueña, No.6 from Recuerdos de Viaje Albéniz
Venetian Gondola Song, Op.30, No.6 from Songs Without Words Mendelssohn

Other titles in the Classical Piano Solos Collection *include...*

VOLUME ONE
Seventeen selected pieces, including...
Maple Leaf Rag Scott Joplin
Minuet in C Ludwig van Beethoven
Nocturne Theme from String Quartet No.2 Alexander Borodin
Prelude And Fugue in D Minor Johann Sebastian Bach
Trumpet Voluntary Jeremiah Clarke
Waltz from Serenade For Strings Peter Ilyich Tchaikovsky
Order No. AM91534

VOLUME TWO
Sixteen selected pieces, including...
Chanson De Matin, Op.15, No.2 Edward Elgar
Ecossaise Franz Schubert
Jesu, Joy Of Man's Desiring Johann Sebastian Bach
Mazurka, Op.101b Lennox Berkeley
Musette en Rondeau Jean-Philippe Rameau
Valse Lente from Coppélia Léo Delibes
Order No. AM91535

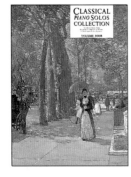

VOLUME FOUR
Seventeen selected pieces, including...
Bagatelle in A Major, Op.33, No.4 Ludwig van Beethoven
Canon César Franck
Humoresque, Op.101, No.7 Antonin Dvořák
Impromptu in A♭, Op.142/D.935, No.2 Franz Schubert
Mazurka in B♭ Major, Op.7, No.1 Frédéric Chopin
Nuages Gris Franz Liszt
Order No. AM91537

VOLUME FIVE
Sixteen selected pieces, including...
Barcarolle from The Seasons Peter Ilyich Tchaikovsky
Intermezzo in E Major, Op.116, No.6 Johannes Brahms
Piano Sonata No.1 in F Minor, Op.2, No.1 Ludwig van Beethoven
Prelude In B Minor, Op.28, No.6 Frédéric Chopin
Rondo Alla Turca from Piano Sonata In A Major, K.331
Wolfgang Amadeus Mozart
Song Without Words In E Major, Op.19, No.1
Felix Mendelssohn-Bartholdy
Order No. AM91538

VOLUME SIX
Fourteen selected pieces, including...
Arabesque No.1 Claude Debussy
Für Elise Ludwig van Beethoven
Mazurka In G Minor, Op.24, No.1 Frédéric Chopin
Prelude from España, Op.165 Isaac Albéniz
Sonatina In C, Op.36, No.3 Muzio Clementi
Variations On 'Ah vous dirai-je Maman', K.265
Wolfgang Amadeus Mozart
Order No. AM91539

ISBN 0-7119-37

Wise Publications
Order No. AM91536

9 780711 937